MY FAVORITE LETTER
The Alphabet Comes Alive!

Written by Susan Gilpin
Illustrated by Hailey Footer

First paperback edition December 2020

Library of Congress Control Number: 2020922575

ISBN 978-0-9970942-1-3 (hardback)
ISBN 978-0-9970942-2-0 (paperback)
ISBN 978-0-9970942-3-7 (ebook)

Published by Possibility Lady Press
Portland, Oregon
www.thepossibilitylady.com

For my mother and father

INTRODUCTION

I love to read and I love words and I love letters, the basic building blocks of language. I have always had impressions of the various letters and mental pictures of their personalities, and I wondered if other people do, too.

I asked people—friends and family and folks on my website—what their favorite letter is and why. And they responded from around the world, ages 5 to 95, about their thoughts, feelings, and reactions to the 26 letters. What do you think about individual letters? Do they make you feel a certain way? Which ones are fun to write? What do they look like or remind you of? Teachers put it to their classes, parents to their children. And it turns out we do have favorites!

This little book is the result of that exploration.

Abracadabra—welcome to the magic of A! It is the Eiffel Tower of the alphabet and just as famous.

It is at the beginning when things are new and strong, and people are fresh and most excited. We feel independent and open to adventure. In school, we like getting As and teachers like giving them, too. An A makes us feel successful, worthy, and proud. A means the best.

Capital A is angular, with clean, sharp edges, and it is the only letter with a triangle in the middle of it. There are two ways to make a little A—**a**, how we learn in school, and **a**, how it looks in most books. And doesn't this cute little **a** look like a person bent over in a yoga pose?

Favorite A words: avocado, art, alphabet, angel, apple, autumn, affection, anteater, astronaut, Aladdin, anything

What is your favorite A word? _____

B is the happiest letter! It is the life of the party and funny, like a big bumble bee buzzing from blossom to blossom.

We like the look of a capital B. It's like a cartoon. It has a nice straight back and then a happy body. It's well-fed. And a small b is a perfect knock-off of its big brother. It's got all the power and none of the extra baggage. It just scoots along.

B has a nice ring to it when it begins a word—*boppity-bop*. But lots of words have a B where it doesn't make a sound. That's when B snuggles up to M—climb, comb, crumb, thumb, and tomb. And then there's the quiet B with T—debt, doubt, and subtle.

Favorite B words: bee, brave, bonanza, bumpkin, book, Belle, buckaroo, bogeyman, beautiful, butterfly, bingo, butt

What is your favorite B word? _____

Can you believe how curious a letter C is, coming on strong in the building blocks of ABC?

The shape of a C shows up in many other letters—d, g, and q—and it's half of an O. It has hard and soft sounds, like candy and circle.

C is practical and also graceful and fluid, just like a cat, which is one of the first words we learn to read. It is cute and curvy, yet cunning and cantankerous.

And in cooking, we have all sorts of wonderful things to eat—cakes, cookies, and caramel apples! Can you think of another C food? _____

Favorite C words: cupcake, cattywampus, can, crayon, Cinderella, color, clodhopper, cha-cha-cha, cucumber, Coke

What is your favorite C word? _____

Don't you love delightful D?

D looks like a smiling fat person, especially when you turn it on its curvy side. D is useful in emoticons. ;D

It would be hard to ask questions without D. We couldn't ask, "Did you have fun today?" And we couldn't say important things to people, such as, "Don't forget to tie your shoes."

We would not have a lot of our favorite creatures without D— dog, donkey, duck, dingo, dodo, deer, dolphin, dove, and dragonfly. And we definitely would not have some of our dearest flowers—daffodil, dahlia, daisy, daphne, delphinium—and that wonderful weed, dandelion.

Favorite D words: duck, dilly-dally, donut, day, do-re-mi, discombobulated, delightful, Dracula, ding-dong, dinosaur

What is your favorite D word? _____

E is everywhere and in almost everything.

An uppercase E is wonderfully geometric and it looks more horizontal than vertical, which is unusual for a capital letter. It feels proud, like a woman standing tall.

The lowercase e is really cute and so different from the capital. It is a happy little friend, and e looks like it is smiling.

E is the most commonly used letter in the alphabet. Here's a challenge: write a sentence at least five words long without using the letter E. For example: "That black dog barks a lot."

_____.

Favorite E words: elephant, emoji, egghead, elbow, Eeyore, email, exaggerate, extra, energy, empty, elf, emoticon

What is your favorite E word? _____

F is a fabulous letter, but we sometimes feel sorry for it because it doesn't have a bottom, like an E that got cut off and might fall over.

However, a capital F is one of the most beautiful of all the letters in calligraphy.

And a cursive lowercase F is also fun to write because of its double loops—it is the only letter that goes both above and below the writing line.

F starts off some wonderful words that make all the difference in the world—fantastic, friend, fun, and fellowship. F is also famous for being naughty.

Favorite F words: fireworks, funny, friend, fancy, freaky, Frankenstein, fairy, freedom, female, falafel, fink, fake

What is your favorite F word? _____

G is the favorite letter of lots of people because it is the start of some of their favorite words—grace, God, grandma and grandpa—and these words make them feel peaceful and blessed. For that reason, G has a more spiritual nature than any of the other letters.

You can't help smiling when you say G out loud. Try it. But sometimes G doesn't want to make a peep, so it stays quiet—gnu, sign, gnome, foreign, gnat. G is tricky like that.

Lowercase G is one of the few letters that can be written in two ways—**g** as we learn in school, or **g** as we see in books.

Favorite G words: gorilla, gratitude, gesundheit, gee whiz, gobbledygook, gopher, genie, green, gibberish, giant, goober

What is your favorite G word? _____

H is for home. It even looks like a house, doesn't it?

H is special because it can be silent. We don't pronounce the H in honor, hour, honest, and heir. We don't say it after the G in ghost, ghastly, gherkin, and ghetto, and we also don't say it after the R in rhinoceros, rhubarb, rhythm, and rhyme.

Hs are stable, happy, and friendly. There is something hilarious and loud about them.

We need H for happy and help and hippopotamus and heart. The world would be sad without these things. We couldn't tell a joke because there would be no humor.

Favorite H words: hat, home, hunky-dory, hotdog, hush, hopscotch, Halloween, hubbub, ha-ha-ha, hocus-pocus

What is your favorite H word? _____

I is interesting and important. It is the only letter besides A that can stand alone as a word. It means me. I is selfish, but it is also proud and independent because of its individuality.

An uppercase I is as plain as it can be, with a tiny horizontal line sometimes added to its top and bottom just to give it a little more character. The lowercase I is fun because it has two parts— a straight line and a polka dot on top! And the name for that little dot is *tittle*.

And even though I is the shortest word (along with *a*), some of the biggest and longest words begin with it—inappropriate, impossibility, and interchangeability.

Favorite I words: igloo, ice skates, icing, imagination, Ichabod, itch, important, Inca, insect, ignoramus, interesting

What is your favorite I word? _____

Just where would we be without J? We couldn't jump for joy, for one thing.

There's something jaunty and swinging about J, like a dandy man with an attitude all dressed up in a top hat.

J is an important letter in names. Without it, we wouldn't have a lot of friends like Jack, Jennifer, James, Julia, Josh, John, Jamie, and Jessica. We would also lose some great months—January, June, and July—and then where would we be? The year would be over too soon!

Favorite J words: jewel, jaunty, jump, Jell-O, joyful, jiffy, Jupiter, justice, jeepers-creepers, jiggle, juicy, jinx, jolt, jet, jam

What is your favorite J word? _____

K is fun and it is the funniest letter of all.

It looks good, too, having a nice straight back with an arm ready to reach up and a sturdy leg to kick with. K is a strong and playful letter, quirky in a friendly way.

K is sometimes silent, as in knee and knife. Some K words have both a silent K and a hard K—knock, knapsack, knuckle—and those are the best K words of all.

Some people do not like K, but those people don't understand that words with K in them are automatically funny—chicken, pickle, mukluk, snorkel, pumpkin, dik-dik, and Kalamazoo. You can't say these words and be angry.

Favorite K words: kite, kind, kiss, kitten, king, kerfuffle, kabob, kibble, kaffeeklatsch, keyboard, Kool-Aid

What is your favorite K word? _____

L is gentle. It is often at or near the end of words used as adjectives to help describe something. For example, adorable, laughable, personal, and magical are helpful words that make our lives more livable.

Writing a capital L in cursive is fun for a lot of people. They enjoy its gentle flow and curviness.

But L can be boring. After all, a little L is just a straight line—l—and so it sometimes gets mixed up with capital I or the number 1. When two Ls get together, however, the fun begins—parallel, tortoiseshell, smelly, belly.

Favorite L words: lion, love, laugh, lightning, likeable, loose, length, lively, lollygag, lull, lackluster, living, lucky, lol

What is your favorite L word? _____

M is tied with S for being the most favorite letter of all! It begins the first word in many languages that anyone ever says when they're a baby—mama.

A capital M is big, twice the size of N, in fact. It's well-balanced and sturdy, and it's the letter to pick for protection. With an M on either side, no harm can come. M is also a 2-for-1 letter—turn it upside down and you have a W.

A small m is delightful. It's like two happy fingers, and when you put some together, they make a yummy comforting sound—mmmm.

Favorite M words: moon, mother, mummy, maze, Mulan, M&Ms, monkey, macaroni, machine, monster, museum, magic

What is your favorite M word? _____

N is not a real favorite, which is sad for this nice letter because it is really important in the alphabet.

Without N we wouldn't have contractions, nor would we have neither and nor. We would still be sledding, slurping, sleeping, eating, reading, and burping, but we would have to figure out a different way of saying those things without our necessary N. And sometimes N doesn't want to be heard—hymn, solemn, autumn. N is a trickster, for sure.

It would be impossible to go next door or live in a neighborhood or visit New York or see birds in a nest. Mr. Edgar Allen Poe's raven would have nothing to say.

Favorite N words: nest, nice, nothing, Netflix, nutty, new, nope, nincompoop, nifty, novel, normal, Neptune, NASA

What is your favorite N word? _____

O say, can you see what a perfect letter O is? O is whole and protected. It can elicit surprise or awe—*oh* and *ooh*!

An O is complete—a nice round circle, no end, on and on and on it goes, and it's easy to make.

O makes you think of people sitting in a circle, around a campfire talking to each other. It's a 3-ring circus and good round things to eat—donuts, cookies, cake, pizza, and oranges.

O turns a bad word into a wonderful, happy word of greeting—hello! Words having double-Os are excellent—pool, football, goose, book, and boo. And where would storytelling be without *Once upon a time*?

Favorite O words: owl, oops, orangutan, over, OMG, optimistic, opposite, onomatopoeia, oblong, outhouse, Oscar

What is your favorite O word? _____

P packs a powerful punch. Put your hands in your pockets and take a peek at P, one of the favorite letters of all children. Find out for yourself and ask a child why.

P produces many good feelings—pride in doing things well, pleasure in playing the piano or petting a puppy, and peaceful when you lay your head on the pillow at night.

P is everywhere in the garden, too—pots of petunias, pansies, peonies, primroses, and phlox. And look there! P has a nifty trick of staying quiet when an H bumps up next to it—photo and pharmacy. It also stays silent when it's followed by an N or S— pneumonia and psychology. And it never makes a peep in the middle of receipt.

Favorite P words: planet, poppycock, Peter Pan, pickle, pony, poop, powderpuff, pajamas, pow-wow, piggybank

What is your favorite P word? _____

Quirky Q is another popular letter. People like it because it is round and fat and has a tail.

Q is jaunty, dashing, devil-may-care, fancy, feminine, and old-fashioned, all at the same time. Q is the start of something unknown, a possible adventure or mystery.

At the same time, there is a bit of smugness to Q's personality, probably because of its unique tail. But Q is also needy—it can't go anywhere without U tagging along.

The lowercase q looks nothing like the capital—in fact, it looks more like a little g without the bottom curve. It is quite calm compared to its big, extravagant sister.

Favorite Q words: queen, quack, quiet, quest, quizzical, question, quarantine, quixotic, quick, quilt, Quasimodo, quality

What is your favorite Q word? _____

Rr

R is wild with a spine—a slope, then a jump with skis.
R is fun because it has a straight line and then a curve and a squiggly, and it takes two taps of the pencil to create.

R is like P but with another leg to stand on. And that leg looks like it is running. R is motion. Run, rabbit, run!

R is a royal and racy robot and it's Robert, the really rapid reader. Or, as Bugs Bunny likes to say, R is a "wascally wabbit."

Favorite R words: rabbit, robot, right, Rumpelstiltskin, rumble, rock-and-roll, Rapunzel, rub-a-dub-dub, run, rocket

What is your favorite R word? _____

S is tied with M for being our very favorite letter!

S is happy and adventurous. It changes the room—S walks in and the party starts. S means more. It is alone, but everyone wants it to join their team because it means they instantly become plural and more is always better.

People like S because it is easy and fun to write in all ways—printing, cursive, and calligraphy. It makes us think of winding roads, meandering paths, and slithering snakes.

S is simple and elegant like a smooth sculpture. It is open-ended and never-ending and soft, with no hard lines or sharp angles. It is half the number 8.

Favorite S words: snake, scuttlebutt, smile, silly, Santa, Saturday, shazam, Superman, switcheroo, sun, sky, skedaddle

What is your favorite S word? _____

T is a trusted servant of the alphabet, but it's not a real favorite letter.

Too bad! T is tried and true, a real workhorse. Lots of stories begin with T—*the* and *there*—and T also is the start of lots of other common words—*this*, *that*, *then*, and *to*. We see lots of Ts on every page. How many can you count here? _____

Without T we would be living in the past because we wouldn't have today, tonight, or tomorrow. Or Thanksgiving. That would be terrible!

T is a very straightforward letter, simple and easy to make. And then there is the silent T. Listen—a whistle!

Favorite T words: tomato, teeter-totter, toot, thanks, tomboy, trick-or-treat, tic-tac-toe, truck, T-rex, touchdown

What is your favorite T word? _____

U is another letter at the bottom of the heap of favorites.

It's easy to make and it's useful because it looks like it could hold a lot—maybe candy, or it could be a fish tank.

U used to be interchangeable with V, and it didn't become a proper letter of its own until about 400 years ago, which is very young, so it's really a baby letter. Now U is quite popular because people use it in texting and written slang instead of *you*. U know who U R, for example.

Favorite U words: umbrella, up, under, unique, unzip, understand, unicorn, underwear, upside-down, umpire, universe

What is your favorite U word? _____

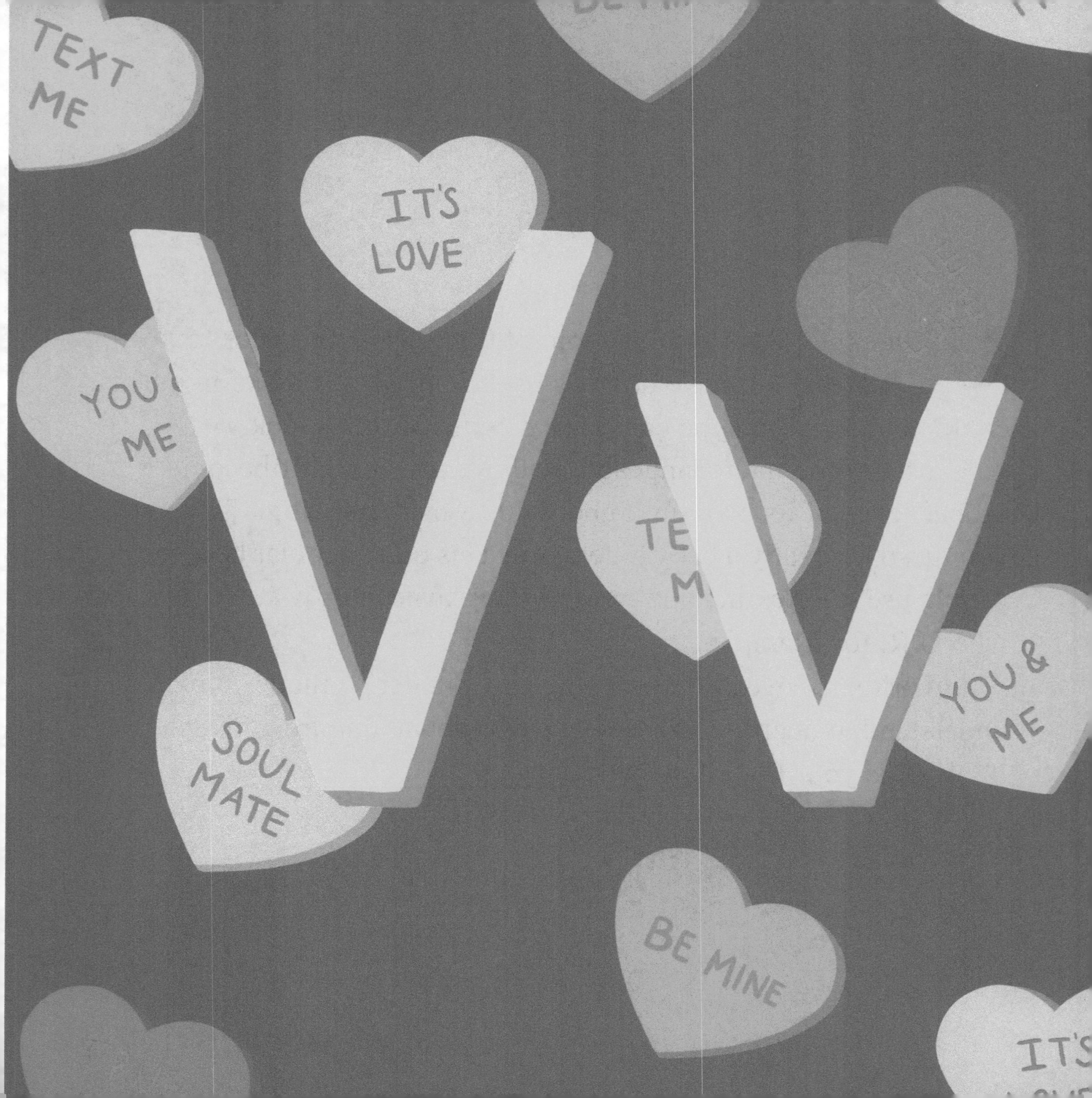
V v
TEXT ME
IT'S LOVE
SOUL MATE
YOU & ME
BE MINE

Very sad, but V is not a favorite letter. In fact, many people don't even like V at all! They say the cursive little V is the worst when writing, especially if it is followed by an i. Try it. You'll see what they mean.

V is a challenging letter to play in word games, but it is useful in making all sorts of wonderful adjectives, like explosive, attractive, expensive, repulsive, positive, and creative.

V is simple to make and looks very fearsome, like a deep valley or an upside-down mountain. V is harsh, a trap.

Favorite V words: valentine, very, victory, venison, verb, volume, valiant, vote, vivacious, vivid, vagabond, viva, vampire

What is your favorite V word? _____

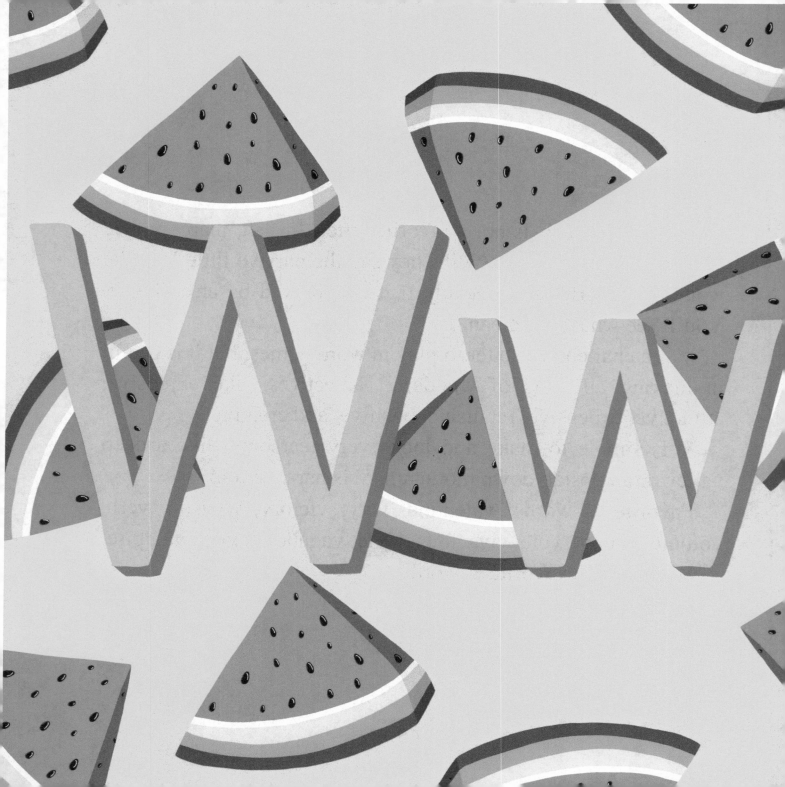

What a happy and wonderful letter we have in W, and one that is really popular.

People like the sound. It takes three times longer to say than any of the other letters—double-U. And that is puzzling because it's really double-V. People also like writing W—the way it starts at the top, goes down, goes up, down again, and finally up again. W is like life.

W makes people feel happy, hopeful, creative, and optimistic, like a person raising their arms to the sky. It is open to possibilities. W is watching waves and wondrous mountains, and when you turn it upside-down, it becomes an M.

Favorite W words: watermelon, wonderful, wow, wish, why, www, wisdom, whippersnapper, who, woodpecker, wink

What is your favorite W word? _____

X—we love X! It brings up feelings of fun and mystery.

X is the most versatile and probably the oldest letter of them all. "X marks the spot" is for people who cannot write—X is good enough for a signature.

X is one of the first letters a child learns to write, but one of the hardest to learn to use because of its many purposes. It is used in algebra (the unknown), genetics (female chromosome), and spirituality, where X means Christ, as in Xmas. It also means poison, as shown by the skull and crossbones. You can't play tic-tac-toe without X. And in love notes and texts it represents kisses—xxx.

Favorite X words: xxx, x-ray, xylophone, xenia, xenophobia

What is your favorite X word? _____

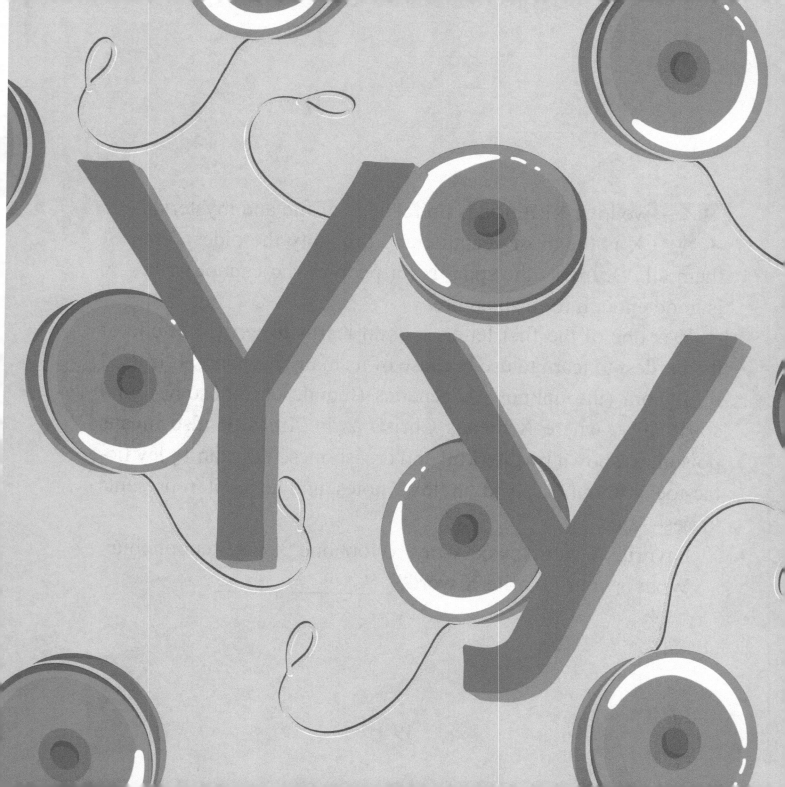

Y is probably the most versatile letter of the alphabet because it is the only one that can be both a vowel and a consonant. On the other hand, Y is wishy-washy because it doesn't really know which one it is. It is a shape-shifter.

People love Y because of its tail, especially in cursive. When Y comes at the end of a word, as it often does, it's fun to add flourishes.

Y is the wishbone, the fork in the road, the empty wineglass. It is the question we ask—why—often enough to have an entire letter of the alphabet named after it.

Favorite Y words: yoyo, yes, yesterday, yahoo, you, yucky, yikes, yellow, yearbook, Yankee, yippee, yabba-dabba-doo

What is your favorite Y word? _____

Z is the last letter of the alphabet. People love Z, and maybe we saved the best for the last. It always pops up at the end—strong and loud.

Z is uncommon and mysterious and risky. And anyone with a Z in their name is automatically fascinating. Z represents snoring—zzz—and Zorro, and its sharp angles make it easy to write.

In Canada and England, they like Z so much that they call it *zed*. No other letter in the alphabet has two different names.

Favorite Z words: zebra, Zorro, zinc, Zanzibar, zero, zap, zing, zig-zag, zillion, zoom, zilch, zippy, zeal, zonk, zombie

What is your favorite Z word? _____

FUN FACTS

Our favorite letters in order of popularity are:

M, S
A, E
K, Q, W
G
B, C
L, O, R, X, Z
H, J, P, Y
D, F, N
I, T, U, V

Even though **F**, **Q**, and **X** made the list of favorites, they are also tied as people's least favorite letters.

Over one-third of the respondents picked the initial letter of their first or last name (but usually the first name) as their favorite letter.

ACKNOWLEDGEMENTS

Thank you for reading about the letters of the alphabet and why people have their favorites. Special thanks to: Abby, Aju, Ali, Amy, Anastasia, Andy, Ann, Anne, Aras, Aron, Becky, Bethany, Cameron, Candace, Celeste, Chris, Corrine, Cynthia, David, Deborah, Declan, Don, Dougie, Eduardo, Elizabeth, Ellie, Erika, Erin, Frank, George, Gillian, Greg, Hailey, Hal, Heather, Irene, Ivan, Jaci, John, Jon, Josh, Judy, Julie, Karyl, Kathy, Kelly, Leon, Lois, Lori, Lynn, Madge, Marcia, Martha, Mary, Maya, Melanie, Nancy, Patty, Philippe, Polly, Sally, Sam, Sarah, Selena, Stephanie, Sue, Virginia, Wendy, Wes, Westley, William, and Ms. W's 4th grade class.

Now the question is—what is YOUR favorite letter?

Please tell me all about it by sending the form on the next page to 2einportland@gmail.com. Let's see your name in the next book!

If you liked reading My Favorite Letter, you will also like the coloring book, which is coming soon. Complete the form on the next page to be notified when it is available.

MY FAVORITE LETTER

Name: _____

Email: _____

City and State (optional): _____

Age (optional): _____

1. What is your favorite letter in the alphabet?

2. What is it you particularly like about this letter?

3. How does it make you feel?

4. What images come to mind? Describe its personality.

5. What is your favorite word beginning with this letter?

6. Do you have negative feelings about any letter(s) and if so, why?

7. Are there other letters you would like to comment on?
Please return your answers to Susan Gilpin at
2einportland@gmail.com.

ABOUT THE AUTHOR

Susan Gilpin is a writer and imaginative entrepreneur, creator of Bespoke Bingo, the Perpetual Calendar of Endless Possibilities, and When I Retire at Night. She lives in Portland, Oregon with a cat named Casey. www.thepossibilitylady.com.

ABOUT THE ILLUSTRATOR

Hailey Footer is a graphic artist who lives in West Linn, Oregon with her husband, three children, and dog. www.haileyfooter.com.

CPSIA information can be obtained
at www.ICGtesting.com
Printed in the USA
BVHW012049121220
595570BV00043B/248